WITCH in STITCHES

KAYE UMANSKY
Illustrated by Judy Brown

PUFFIN BOOKS

For Mo and Ella

PUFFIN BOOKS

Published by the Penguin Group
27 Wrights Lane, London W8 5TZ, England
Viking Penguin Inc., 40 West 23rd Street, New York, New York 10010, USA
Penguin Books Australia Ltd, Ringwood, Victoria, Australia
Penguin Books Canada Ltd, 2801 John Street, Markham, Ontario, Canada L3R 1B4
Penguin Books (NZ) Ltd, 182–190 Wairau Road, Auckland 10, New Zealand

Penguin Books Ltd, Registered Offices: Harmondsworth, Middlesex, England

First published 1988

Made and printed in Great Britain by
Cox and Wyman Ltd, Reading, Berks.
Filmset in Linotron 202 Futura, Palatino and Rockwell by
Rowland Phototypesetting Ltd, Bury St Edmunds, Suffolk

▮ CONTENTS ▮

CONTENTS

A Letter from your Editor, Witch Pickins

Hello, Witches everywhere! What a week it's been! Sackfuls of letters from vexed Vampires, phone calls at midnight from indignant Ghosts, bricks through the window from glowering Goblins, crowds of Skeletons trying to beat my front boulder down, being pelted with green slime every time I venture out, a black eye from a particularly incensed Yeti – and why? All because *Witches in Stitches* is so popular. You see, our great magazine is the ONLY one of its kind. It seems that all you other inferior-type monsters out there just haven't got what it takes to produce a magazine of your own. Therefore, by popular request, and because I'm tired of being hit by bricks, *Witches in Stitches* proudly announces that from now on, it will open its pages to non-witches. Yes, you lucky old Ghouls and Zombies and other unsavoury types – at last you're going to have some pages of your own!

Meet my great new team of specialist sub-editors, who'll be responsible for their own boring bits.

■ INTRODUCTORY POEM

The Witches got together
One year, at Hallowe'en;
They thought they'd have a bit of fun
And start a magazine.

The idea proved a great success,
Of that there is no doubt:
The Monsters queued to snap it up,
The bookshops soon sold out.

'It's wonderful!' the readers wrote,
'We love it! Give us more!
No one has ever bothered
With the likes of us before.'

The Goblins got the giggles,
The Phantoms were in fits,
The Skeletons were doubled up
And laughed themselves to bits.

The Vampires smiled politely
In the way that Vampires do –
And the Witches were in stitches
All the long night through.

CONTENTS

▌LIMERICK

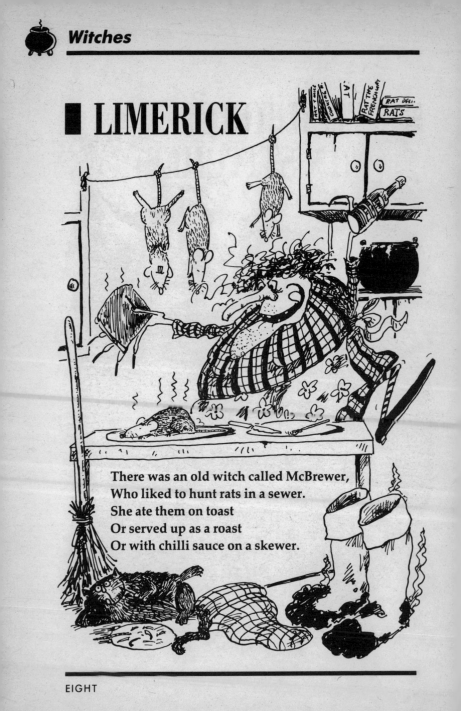

There was an old witch called McBrewer,
Who liked to hunt rats in a sewer.
She ate them on toast
Or served up as a roast
Or with chilli sauce on a skewer.

■ WITCH JOKES

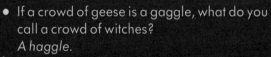

- If a crowd of geese is a gaggle, what do you call a crowd of witches?
  A haggle.
- Where do witches cook their dinner?
  In the coven.
- What do witch brooms like to eat?
  Bristle sprouts.
- What did the sad broom do?
  Went into a corner and swept.
- Heard of the broom with the stiff stick?
  It suffered from broomatism.
- If a broom has a temperature, can it be 'flu?
  Not until it's better.

CAULDRON FRILL!

Another frilling idea from Rubbish-By-Post Ltd!

Is your cauldron a pretty sight? Or is it the usual ancient, black, rusting, dented, stew-encrusted, rank smelling blot on the landscape? Cauldron Frills are a new, exciting idea. They come in a wide range of pretty Victorian-look fabrics that will add a touch of class to any cauldron, however sordid. Choose from a host of TWO – yes, **TWO** – delightful designs, including:

Country Nettle Patch (with tasteful cow pat border)

Scummy Pond (Charming frog motif. Unusual shade of green)

Be the envy of all your friends. Just fill in the coupon, and Rubbish-By-Post will rush your frill to you by registered broom immediately.

Yes please! I cannot live another day without my cauldron frill.

Name _____

Address _____

_____

■ WHAT'S COOKING?
with Eva Froggin

Hi there, Witches! Eva Froggin here, your very own Witch Cook, with two new mouth-watering recipes for you to try. Remember my recipe for success?

a. Encourage flies into your cave by keeping a large pile of horse manure at the entrance. Remember, Flies Add Flavour.

b. If you must wash up, save the water for gravy.

c. **Never wash your hands.**

Happy eating, girls!

Crispmouse Cake

12 oz ready-mixed maggots
1 level teaspoon dried tadpoles
1 lb earwigs
½ slug (sliced)
1 ripe mouse
juice of a large lemming
½ pint frog spawn

1. Thoroughly grease a rusty old bucket.
2. Mix all the dry ingredients – maggots, tadpoles, earwigs –
together in a dirty bowl.

3. In a separate, dirtier, bowl cream together the sliced slug and lemming juice.

4. Gradually add the frog spawn until you have a revolting slimy mess. Sneeze in it for luck. Add this to the dry mix.

5. Now take your mouse. Put it through the mouse mincer. Save the tail for decoration. Add the minced mouse to the other muck you've already prepared.

6. Throw the whole slop into the bucket, and bake over a low fire until burnt and crispy.

7. When black and smouldering, turn out on to sheet of old newspaper.

8. Place the coiled mouse tail artistically in the centre, and sprinkle with little red ladybirds for that professional touch.

Toad Tart

1 large, fresh stewing toad
¼ lb toadstools
1 teaspoon bedbugs
pinch of bat droppings

For the pastry:
6 oz dried beetle do's
3 oz best frog fat
2 tablespoons ditch water

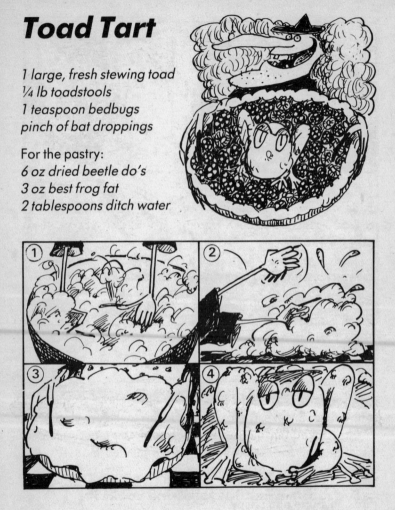

1. Rub frog fat into beetle do's. Add ditch water.
2. Thump well and roll out on dirty floor.
3. Use it to line a dustbin lid.
4. Place toad in middle.

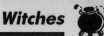

5. Sprinkle with toadstools.
6. Add bedbugs and bat droppings. Cook slowly. Serve with a green salad.

■ Next week, Eva's recipes include:

Moley Voley Pudding
Ferret Fingers
Baked Snake (perfect for long business lunches)

■ Eva recommends the following books for your shelf:

Witch Fish Recipes by Poppy Nanoot
Italian Witch Dishes by Maura Wormsa
Witch Food on a Budget by Stuart Oast

■ POETRY CORNER

I'm sick of that Hansel and Gretel

I'm sick of that Hansel and Gretel,
Those couple of kids make me sick.
If they knock at my door,
I'll give 'em what for,
I'll be waiting for them with a brick.

They come wandering up to my sweet house
(And building that house took a week),
Between 'em they wrecked it,
But when I objected
They go and complain. What a cheek!

The fuss people make over Hansel!
I ask you, what do you expect?
I wanted him fat
'Cos that boy was a brat,
And, remember, my house had been wrecked.

That Gretel. Oh my, what a baby.
I give her some housework to do.
She cries and she moans,
Then she blubbers and groans,
'Til I wallop her legs. Wouldn't you?

They pushed me inside my own oven.
I'm a Witch. Do they think I'm a fool?
They thought I was dead,
But I just banged my head,
And it took me six months to get cool.

We Witches are always made wicked –
I tell you, it gets me real mad.
If I wrote that story,
I'd get all the glory,
But no. I'm the Witch, so I'm bad.

I'm sick of that Hansel and Gretel,
I hope they return very quick,
And when they appear
I'll rush out with a cheer
And polish them off with my brick.

Shopping List

Pound of pickled porcupine
Slug slime spread
Three ripe bull-frogs
One rat (dead)
Large tin of termites
Small bag of flies
Alligator muesli
(Economy size)
Rags to the laundry
Skunk shampoo
Pick up pension
That's it. Phew!

APPLICATION FORM
FOR ENTRY TO COVEN

PER CAULDRA AD ASTRA

Name __Witch Rosa Mouldyteeth__

Address __1 Sewer View__

__Witchwood__

Age __old (ish)__

Witches

Please answer the following questions truthfully.

1 Are you good at spelling? ~~sey~~ ~~eys~~ EYS

2 Are you sure? ~~oK~~ ~~No~~ EYS

3 Spell the following words, then, clever:

witch _Wij_

cauldron _called Ron_

cave _Kayf_

broom _brume_

4 Do you have your own broom? If so, please give the following details:

Name _Crazy Neville_

Colour _usualy brown. Goes white before a crash Landing_

Registration number _NEV 1_

Any serious personality problems?

stark raving bonkers

5 How long have you been flying?

on Neville? too long

Any serious accidents? *49 crash landings*
50 mid-air pile-ups, 368 refusals,
various fights with hot-air
balloons etc. I could rite a book.

6 Are you interested in any of the following sports:

YES	NO	
☐	☑	Bonfire leaping
☐	☑	Inter-coven friendly fights
☑	☐	Inter-coven unfriendly fights
☑	☐	Goblin bashing
☑	☐	Mouse mashing
☑	☐	Frog squashing

7 How would you turn a porcupine into a
man-eating shark? Give details

very, very carefully

8 Describe briefly your worst-ever bad deed

attempting to saw up Neville

9 If you weren't a Witch, what would you
choose to be, and why?

I would be _a Nanny, i love little
children (boiled, scrambled,
any way
reelly)_

10 Complete the following sentence:
I wish to join this coven because

_like Neville, I am
compleety loony_

WITCHES IN STITCHES
HALLOWE'EN HOP

- All Witches welcome
- The most fashionable event in the Witch calendar!
- Top celebrities from the world of magic
- Barbecue (hot frogs, hamsterburgers, rats on a stick, etc.) charred to a cinder by Eva Froggin
- Make-up demonstration by beauty expert Tina Polyfilla
- 'Down with Goblins' designer T-shirts for sale: all proceeds go to a bad cause (Royal Society for the Prevention of Goblins)
- Dance the night away to Mad Madge and the Barmy Banshee Girls, the hottest new sounds around
- All sorts of fun games, including Broom Racing, Unlucky Dip, Pass the Porcupine, Musical Bats and Hunt the Kipper
- The ever-popular Goblin Bashing begins on the dot of midnight, so don't be late
- See you there!

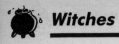

■ THE WITCH LAW

A Witch must always do her worst,
Show no consideration.
A Witch must always come out first
In every situation.
A Witch must cheat and use foul play.
A Witch cannot be trusted.
She does a bad turn every day
And **must be dirt-encrusted**.

■ THE WITCH CODE

- Keep your broom under close control at all times.

- Daylight flying is forbidden, especially round airports.

- **Always** look filthy. Anyone caught owning a flannel faces a heavy fine.

- **Never, ever, under any circumstances**, be pleasant to a Goblin.

- Sweet houses need planning permission from the Witch Council.

- Familiars should be discouraged from eating each other. It is bad manners. Besides, clearing up a load of chewed toad first thing in the morning is most unpleasant.

- Always return spell books to the library on time. Witches caught scribbling on them, tearing out pages or using them to beat Goblins over the head will be banned from the library.

- Dwarf sightings should be reported **immediately**. Take a note of their names (Grumpy, Dopey, etc.) and number (e.g. 7), and inform the Witch Council, who will take steps to remove them from the area.

- What you wear in private is your affair, but boots, shoes and hats must be worn out.

- Children called Hansel, Gretel, Snow White or Dorothy are Bad News. Avoid them like the plague.

- Remember to inform your neighbours if you intend spending the night cavorting, cackling and generally carrying on under the moon. A polite threatening note works wonders.

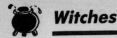

■ EXCLUSIVE! A Letter from

The Palace
Tuesday

Dear Snow White,

I expect you're surprised to get a letter from me after all this time, darling, I just felt it was time to let bygones be bygones, and clear up one or two misunderstandings.

You'll be pleased to hear I've sent that silly old mirror back to the manufacturers. There is no doubt in my mind that it was faulty, and the cause of our little differences. It seems a pity to let a little thing like a malfunctioning mirror spoil our friendship, doesn't it?

Now. You know that old woman who came to your door with the ribbons, dear? And the one with the comb? And the rosy cheeked peasant woman with the poisoned apple? Well, none of them were me. Really. They were all cases of mistaken identity. I was here in the Palace all the time, telling off that cloth-eared huntsman who must have misheard my instructions. I never told him to kill you with a demon blade, dearest. In fact, I told him to fill you with lemonade. I'd made some specially. Oh well, that's all water under the bridge. You're quite safe now, and married to Prince

the Wicked Queen to Snow White

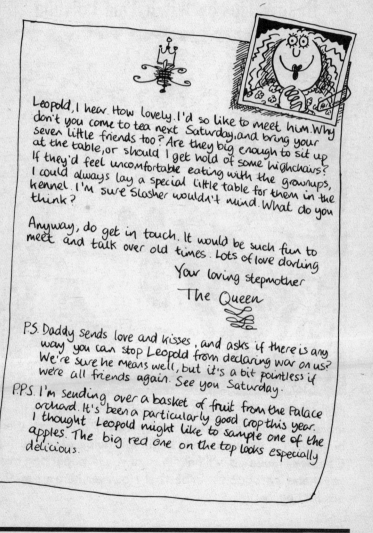

Leopold, I hear. How lovely. I'd so like to meet him. Why don't you come to tea next Saturday, and bring your seven little friends too? Are they big enough to sit up at the table, or should I get hold of some highchairs? If they'd feel uncomfortable eating with the grownups, I could always lay a special little table for them in the kennel. I'm sure Slasher wouldn't mind. What do you think?

Anyway, do get in touch. It would be such fun to meet and talk over old times. Lots of love darling

Your loving stepmother

The Queen

P.S. Daddy sends love and kisses, and asks if there is any way you can stop Leopold from declaring war on us? We're sure he means well, but it's a bit pointless if we're all friends again. See you Saturday.

P.P.S. I'm sending over a basket of fruit from the Palace orchard. It's been a particularly good crop this year. I thought Leopold might like to sample one of the apples. The big red one on the top looks especially delicious.

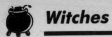
■ LOOKING GOOD?

Beauty Tips by Witch Tina Polyfilla

Hello there, fans! You Witches are always asking me how I manage to look so radiant and perfectly groomed. Well, being incredibly attractive to begin with helps, of course. No amount of make-up will help most of you. A paper bag over your head is probably your best bet. However, here are my ten tips for beauty.

1 A good deep-down cleanse is very important for a glowing complexion. I rub down with sandpaper first, then carefully fill in the wrinkles with good-quality cement. I then massage my face with a mixture of Gerbil Spit and Crushed-grub Washing Grains. I couldn't live without my moisturizer! I find very old chip fat works best on my delicate skin.

2 My most important make-up item is my lipstick. My favourite colour is Sludgy Pond, although Iguana Green looks good with a tan.

3 You hair is _so_ important. Malcolm, my hairdresser, is a genius. His speciality is the Exploding Bird's Nest, which I feel rather suits me. Between yearly washes, I revive it with mouse mousse, which has a pleasant, cheesy smell.

4 Here's a useful little hint. If, like me, you are lucky enough to have one or two good-sized warts on your face, try painting them different colours. I call it Wart Art. It really makes them stand out on those special occasions! If you don't have any warts, try doing what you can with a bad boil or pimple.

5 Perfume is so feminine. My favourite is 'Night in a Fish Factory'. A little goes such a long way. If you really want to splash out, go for one of the more expensive brands, such as 'Eau de Blocked Drain', or the wonderful 'Skunk Drops'.

6 People often remark on my hands. 'Tina,' they say, 'your hands are wonderful. Just how do you keep them looking so good?' Well, the answer is an age-old family remedy. I never do any washing-up. Occasionally, every half hour or so, I give myself a manicure. I soak my hands in swamp water for a few minutes, then sharpen the nails on a scratch pad. I make sure the dirt is well pushed down before applying several coats of Scum Green, my favourite shade of nail varnish.

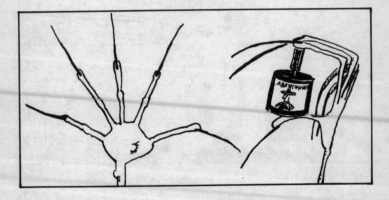

7 To shave or not to shave? That is the question. Personally, I prefer to be clean-shaven, otherwise people tend not to notice my warts. But some of you may find a light stubble suits you, or even a full set of whiskers. It's a personal choice. If you *do* decide to copy me, which I suppose most of you will, do use a sharp razor. There's nothing more unsightly than walking around with dirty little bits of torn-up newspaper stuck all over your chin.

8 Looking good is all about feeling good. I keep in shape by taking regular exercise and eating well. I regularly bash up a Goblin before breakfast. If I miss a morning, I make sure that the next day I bash up two. I've learnt to say no to fatty foods (such as rhino blubber — fatal!) and sweet things, like Bee Bars, Candied Cockroach and Mice Cream. Instead, I munch on delicious crispy Tadpole Tails, which are much less fattening.

9 The other day I received a letter from a fan inquiring whether I ever brushed my tooth! Are you mad? Teeth should be black, rotten, and ideally most should be missing. If you can't encourage the last few to drop out (and my last one is most stubborn), ignore them. Remember the old saying? 'The lot will rot if you don't give a jot.' *Brush* them? Don't make me laugh.

10 My final tip is to pin up photographs of someone whose looks you admire all over your cave. It will give you inspiration and make you try harder. My own photo (personally auto-graphed) comes in two sizes, small (10p) or large with frame (£25). Unfortunately, only the large ones are left. Please send your request WITH THE MONEY to:

Witch Tina Polyfilla, Beauty Expert,
Witches in Stitches Magazine

A WITCHES IN STITCHES WEEKEND BREAK!

- Two nights' accommodation in a top cave

- Kick off your boots and tan your old tootsies on our glorious beach with mile after mile of sharp, painful pebbles strewn with slimy seaweed

- Marvel at the unusual jelly-like blobby things with feelers which inhabit the warm rock pools

- Cool your corns in the brown, soupy sea

- Soak up the atmosphere of our local fish factory (makers of the popular perfume)

Great value at just £500! Discover the delights of

BILGEWATER ON SEA

Take a dip, pierce your feet on the pebbles, get buried under an avalanche or eaten by sharks, why should we care as long as we get your £500? The survivors will be taken home in an armoured coach on Sunday evening. A superb weekend discovering the fun of the seaside and a chance to sample our local delicacy (jelly-like blobby things). Just send this coupon for full details now!

To: Witches in Stitches Travel Service,
　　c/o Ripoff Enterprises, PO Box 1, Bilgewater

Please send me full details of the Bilgewater weekend.

Name _____

Address _____

■ CLASSIFIED

LONELY HEARTS

■ Attractive Male Broom
Successful, straight, professional flier, very good-looking, tall, thin, dark bristles, seeks a slim, clean, very attractive young female mop, to enjoy flying out together and spring cleaning. No sponge heads or vacuum cleaners need apply. Photo/phone, please.

■ Romantic Witch
Seeks Very Rich Wizard. I am ravishing, with frizzy hair, boney nose and dozens of cute chin warts. I like soft music, dim lights and RICH food. If you're soft, dim and RICH, you could be for me. I love children and often have one for supper. Why not come and share a kiddy by candlelight, and let me go through your pockets? I'm very sincere and not after you for your money. Write now, enclosing bank statement.

■ Black Cat
Tom, fit, hunky, into mousing, silver-top milk and good-quality fish heads, seeks high-class PEDIGREE female for caring relationship. Own basket and scratch pad. No tacky ginger flea-bitten moggies, PLEASE.

ITEMS FOR SALE

■ Broom
Needs a bit of work. Flying licence expired. A bit of stick warp here & there. Needs new set of bristles. Also has filthy temper & can be stubborn starting on cold mornings. Any offers? Owner will deliver if she can get the swine started.

■ Rat Processor
Skins, slices, chops, crushes, pulps, minces. And that's just your fingers. Needs a good scrape-out, otherwise perfect. Owner will take anything. Needs cash urgently to pay doctor's bills.

■ Cave
Pleasantly cosy. Ideally situated on lower slopes of active volcano, hence low heating bills. Owner in hurry to sell. (Would consider swapping for igloo.)

■ Goblin Teasmaid
Unwanted gift. Incredibly stupid. Answers to the name of Oy You. Couldn't make tea to save his life. Possibly could be trained to be doormat. Comes with own bobble hat and silly pair of trousers.

■ VAMPIRES ■ (IN STITCHES)

Hi! I'm Uncle Drac, and I'm in charge of the Vampire section. It's great to be part of the *Witches in Stitches* team. I've been wanting to get my teeth into something new for ages. Just take a look at what we've got for you.

CONTENTS

■ LIMERICK

A foolish young dentist called Keith
Agreed to clean Dracula's teeth,
No more is he drilling.
Instead, he is filling
A whopping great hole on the heath.

■ A VAMPIRE PLAY

FIRST VAMPIRE: (*Looking in mirror*) This fang's getting blunt. Think I should sharpen it?

SECOND VAMPIRE: (*Shrugging*) I don't see the point.

FIRST VAMPIRE: There isn't a point. That's the point.

SECOND VAMPIRE: (*Looking in first vampire's mouth*) Where? Point to it.

FIRST VAMPIRE: I can't point to a point. There is no point.

SECOND VAMPIRE: Then what's the point of discussing it?

FIRST VAMPIRE: I just wanted your opinion on this point.

SECOND VAMPIRE: I thought there wasn't one.

FIRST VAMPIRE: There isn't. That's my problem.

SECOND VAMPIRE: What is?

FIRST VAMPIRE: This fang's getting blunt. Think I should sharpen it . . . ?

CURTAIN

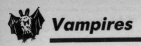

■ QUIZ

So you want to become a Vampire?

Here's a suitability test. Put a tick in the box of your choice.

1. You need to get the teeth right. Would you:
- ☐ **a)** File them yourself with a chisel . . .
- ☑ **b)** Go to a Harley Street dentist . . .
- ☐ **c)** Gargle with tomato ketchup . . .
- ☐ **d)** Wait and see if they change on their own . . .

2. The right image is important. Do you:
- ☐ **a)** Buy a stylish cloak from Horrids . . .
- ☐ **b)** Get a not-so-stylish one from a jumble sale . . .
- ☐ **c)** Cut up your mum's best winter coat . . .
- ☐ **d)** Wear your pale-blue nylon anorak and hope for the best . . .

3. Your mum asks you to tidy your room. Do you:
- ☐ **a)** Hoover your coffin . . .
- ☐ **b)** Sort the bat droppings into labelled boxes . . .
- ☐ **c)** Tastefully arrange the cobwebs . . .
- ☐ **d)** Carefully dust your teddy/pink rabbit/fairy doll . . .

4. Vampires need helpers. Do you:
- ☐ **a)** Make friends with someone called Igor . . .
- ☐ **b)** Make friends with someone who doesn't mind you calling him Igor . . .

☐ **c)** Make friends with someone called Keith who stoops a bit . . .

☐ **d)** Join a choir . . .

5. Have you thought about where to live? Will you:

☐ **a)** Buy a Transylvanian castle . . .

☐ **b)** Squat in a Welsh ruin . . .

☐ **c)** Ask your dad to clear out the cellar . . .

☐ **d)** Move in to your little sister's Wendy House . . .

6. Vampires need blood. Do you:

☐ **a)** Bite the dog . . .

☐ **b)** Hang hopefully around hospitals . . .

☐ **c)** Hide all the Elastoplast and hope someone cuts themselves . . .

☐ **d)** Smother everything with ketchup . . .

Your Suitability Rating

Score 3 for every A you've ticked, 2 for the Bs, 3 for the Cs and 0 for the Ds.

0–6 Suggest you book an appointment for a blood transfusion. You are a goody-goody and will never make a Vampire. Have you considered the cubs or brownies?

6–12 You're a possibility, but you'll have to work at it. Suggest you start in a small way and work up. Try nibbling a hamster. Persuade your local hospital to let you sit in on an operation or two. Don't give up. It's in your blood somewhere.

12–18 You are definite Vampire material. You have real style. Become one immediately. As soon as you're kitted out, find an area that doesn't have a local Vampire, and get to work.

■ MUSIC PAGE

Vampire Song

*(To be sung to the tune of
'My Old Man's a Dustman')*

My Uncle Ted's a Vampire
He wears a Vampire's hat,
And sometimes when it's midnight
He turns into a bat,
So if you hear a tapping
When you're tucked up in bed,
Don't pull the blind,
For you might just find
It's my awful Uncle Ted.

Another Song

*(To be sung to the tune of 'For He's a
Jolly Good Fellow')*

For he's a batty old fellow,
His fangs are furry and yellow.
They're stained with strawberry jello,
But he don't use a brush,
No, he don't use a brush,
You'd think he'd buy a brush,
His breath's inclined to smell-o,
'Cos he don't use a brush.

■ VAMPIRE JOKES

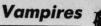

What did the vampire say to his victim?
Your neck's on my list.

Why are vampires so unpopular?
They go round teething people.

What did the vampire say when he got given a
free set of dentures?
Fangs for nothing.

FIRST VAMPIRE: Want some of my blood?
SECOND VAMPIRE: No. I've got clots of my own.

When vampires don't feel like cooking, what do
they do?
Nip out for a quick bite.

Why do bat mums go batty in the morning?
*Because little bats spend so long hanging
around in the batroom.*

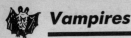

■ KIDS' PAGE

Songs to Sing to Young Vampettes

Jack and Jill

Jack and Jill to Vampire Hill
By Dracula were taken.
Jack, he made a tasty snack,
And Jill was grilled with bacon.

Gory Rory

Gory Rory pudding and pie
Bit the girls and made them cry.
When the boys appeared in view
Gory Rory bit them too.

Three Blind Bats

Three blind bats,
Three blind bats,
See how they flap,
See how they flap.
They all flapped after the farmer's wife
Who buttered the bats with a butter knife,
You never did see such a mess in your life,
As three blind bats.

∎ VAMPIRE PICK-UPS

Beware! Be on your guard if a tall, pale man with a long cloak and an obvious dental problem says any of the following things to you:

1 I've got this sore throat. Can you see anything wrong with it?

2 You've cut your finger? Let me kiss it better.

3 Anyone out there? This lid seems to be stuck, ha ha.

4 Would you mind stepping up this dark alley and taking a look at my car/sewing machine/stamp collection/sick granny/Teasmaid?

5 Wow! Open day at the Blood Bank! Fancy coming along?

6 What, dawn already? Past my bedtime.

7 I was wondering if you could recommend a dentist . . .

8 Sorry to bother you, but I'm doing this survey on blood sports . . .

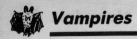
▌ VAMPIRE DIARY

A Week in the Death of Prince Vamp

Monday — Got up at midnight. Shaved teeth. Tidied coffin, oiled hinges. Ate a bowl of Goreflakes. Got letter from Blood Bank. Overdrawn again. Manager's getting nasty. Went for walk to look for victim (preferably manager). Nobody about. Noticed lot of FOR SALE signs. Can't think why. Got caught in storm, like always. Got soaked. Came home. No supper. Quick blood bath, followed by an early day. Hate Mondays.

Tuesday — Filthy cold. Igor called doctor. He said my blood pressure's low. Asked me what I ate. I said necks to nothing. Told me to drink a lot and get plenty of rest. Took him at his word. Nipped, then napped, ha ha. Felt much better. Must remember to look for new doctor.

Wednesday — Horrible breakfast. Igor forgot to buy Goreflakes. All out of Ready Neck too. Made do with Rice Clotties, which I hate. Must have a word with Igor. Felt tired, so took a short coffin break. Got up, went looking for victims again. No suck cess. Went to bed starving.

Thursday Dental appointment 2.30 (tooth hurty, ha ha). Dentist polished my fangs and charged me £10. I must be a sucker. Came back to castle. Igor had cut his finger, so there was lunch. 'Have an accident?' I inquired. Igor said, no, thanks, he'd already had one. Then he painted the kitchen. He always paints at the sight of blood. I wonder about him sometimes.

Friday Run out of Rice Clotties, can you believe! When you think how much castle-keeping money he gets! Made do with a blood orange. Don't go much on vegetarian. Thought about sacking Igor. Looked for sack in shed. Much to my amazement, found shed full of packets of Goreflakes and Ready Neck. More blood shed than garden shed. Igor's secret hoard. What a sneak. And to think I trusted him.

Saturday Mentioned my discovery to Igor. He denies all knowledge, and is threatening strike action. Last time he used a mallet, which struck me rather funny. Looks like I'm stuck with him.

Sunday Stayed in coffin with one of my bad headaches. Heard hammering. Tried to get up, couldn't. Lid won't budge. I can hear Igor out there eating all the Goreflakes. Am writing this in dark. Biro may well have run out. No one may ever read this. He's really nailed me this time.

■ AUNTY COAGULA'S PROBLEM PAGE

Sharing a problem with someone who knows and cares is halfway to solving it. Aunty Coagula, our agony aunt, doesn't care about anything, but write to her anyway at:

**AUNTY COAGULA'S
PROBLEM PAGE
VAMPIRE EXPRESS
TRANSYLVANIA**

Dear Aunty Coagula,

My headstone has the wrong name carved on it. It says:

EBENEZER THUNDERBROW

My name is Norman Slug. You couldn't get much more different. What kind of mistake is that?
Yours,

N. Slug.

AUNTY COAGULA
REPLIES:

It's a grave mistake.

Dear Aunty Coagula,

I am really depressed. My ghoulfriend has left me for a Zombie. My hair's falling out and I've lost my appetite. The other night I just couldn't be bothered to finish drinking my supper. What's happening to me?

AUNTY COAGULA
REPLIES:

Sounds like you've run out of suck. Can I go home now?

Dear Aunty Coagula,

You must help me. I am a Vampire who has this recurring nightmare where a pack of mad air ghostesses in pink nighties are pelting me with fruit cake from a light aircraft. They won't stop and . . . they're getting closer . . . I can hear the engine . . . and I'm running and running . . . and I'm getting raisins in my eyes . . . ahhhh . . . help . . .

AUNTY COAGULA REPLIES:

What a pity you didn't trust me with your name and address. I would have come round personally and dragged you off to the loony bin. No, seriously. Don't worry. Lots of Vampires have these dreams. They're quite normal. You're not, though. See a spookiatrist immediately. As to the air ghostesses – it's only high spirits.

Dear Aunty Coagula,

Here's a beauty tip for all your readers. Try rubbing a mixture of flour, dandruff and dried bat droppings into your skin. It will make you look paler and much more scary, especially if you rub your lips with a mixture of goat's blood, lobster sick and crushed holly berries. Or red smarties.
Yours,

Vein Vampire

AUNTY COAGULA REPLIES:

Looks like another one for the funny farm.

Dear Aunty Coagula,

I know you must be fed up with getting letters about teeth. But here's another one. What sort of razor would you recommend? Or do you prefer sandpaper, or a chisel, or a file? Some of my friends have experimented successfully with heavy-duty pencil sharpeners. Which method do you suggest?

AUNTY COAGULA REPLIES:

Who cares? You're right, to tell the tooth, I'm sick to the teeth of getting toothy problems. So push off, with your daft pencil sharpeners. Take your toothy problems toothy dentist and don't bother me. I only do this job for the blood money anyway.

▮ POETRY CORNER

Poem *by A. Poet*

You might have a mania
For Transylvania,
But it's screamier
In Bohemier.
(In Hull
It's just dull.)

Epitaph

Here lies Dracula.
He's either on his backula
Or standing right behind you,
Getting ready to attackula.

Another Poem *by Anne Notherpoet*

I'm turning into Dracula,
My teeth are getting thinner,
They're really quite spectacular,
It's hard to eat my dinner,
I'm going off my food a bit
(Except for strawberry jam)
My mother says I'm batty,
And she's right. I think I am.

Still Another Poem
by Stella Notherpoet (Anne's sister)

V *is for vein, and it's usually blue,*
A *is for artery (that's for blood too),*
M *is for midnight (the time they get manic),*
P *is for p – p – p – p – p – p – panic,*
I *is for Igor, the vampire's best mate,*
R *is for rusty old blood on a plate,*
E *is for ending. It's over. You're gone.*
So *if you meet a vampire, don't stop, kid. Walk on.*

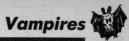

■ HANDY HINTS

Things to Do with a Clapped-out Vampire

A worn out vampire would make a great can opener . . .

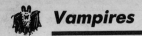

... or a kite ...

... a windmill,
perhaps? ...

. . . or a hole punch . . .

. . . curtains? . . .

. . . or a desk-spike . . .

Vampires

■ SKELETONS ■ (IN STITCHES)

A big hello to all you Skeleton readers. The name's Hank Lanky, and I'm responsible for the Skeleton pages. It's nice to get this job, as, make no bones about it, I've been through some thin times recently. Here's what we've got in store for you.

CONTENTS

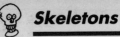

■ LIMERICK

A Skeleton, Fatty O'Hyatt,
Went on a low-calorie diet.
Although he got little,
His bones were so brittle
He snapped. He was silly to try it.

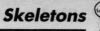

■ BONE JOKES

What instruments do skeletons play?
Xylabones, saxabones and trombones. Never organs. They don't have them.

What do skeletons build on Hallowe'en?
Bonefires.

Who was the famous French lady skeleton who commanded an army?
Bone of Ark.

Heard of the tragedy of the skeleton and his girlfriend?
They broke up. He was shattered.

Who was the famous skeleton who worked herself to skin and bone?
Thinderella.

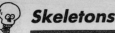
■ SKELETON HISTORY

The Bone Age

Otherwise known as the Golden Age, when Skeletons roamed in gangs over the face of the planet singing loud football songs, spraying Skeleton slogans on rocks, sneering at sabre-toothed tigers and generally bossing everyone else about.

In the early part of the age, they lived in caves, but later it is believed they constructed primitive, low, three-bedroom houses with fitted carpets known as bonegalows.

Their diet consisted of sticky bones, bonanas and at least ten strong cups of tea a day, which they counted very carefully, being teatotallers.

They spent all their time hunting the Cranium – a long-legged water bird which haunted the marshes. Bone Age Skeletons would try and bring this bird to its knees using carved bones known as bonerangs. Luckily, the Cranium was an intelligent bird, and avoided being captured by:

1 Putting it about that it was extinct.
2 Flying away to another country, just to make sure.

Therefore Bone Age Skeletons never tasted this bird. That didn't stop them from holding feast days, when they would sit about with empty plates discussing what the Cranium *might* taste like if they ever succeeded in catching one.

Fire was discovered – hence the word bonefire – and although the wheel wasn't quite there yet, a brilliant Japanese Skeleton named Ad Rib invented the spokes, thus becoming the first official Skeleton spokesman.

The Rattle of Waterloo

This famous Rattle was fought many years ago at Waterloo station, London. Many well-known Skeletons were involved, including Bone of Ark (French), Napoleon Bonypart (also French), Bony Prince Charlie (Scottish) and England's very own James Boned. In order that they could tell each other apart, Bone of Ark and Napoleon wore berets, Bony Prince Charlie wore a kilt and James Boned wore a dustbin lid on his head because he was an undercover agent.

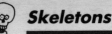

▌ POETRY CORNER

Skeletons on Bicycles

Skeletons on bicycles,
White and cold as icicles,
Rattling like ricicles
Don't look all that nicicles.

Skeletons are Cool

When everyone is sweltering
Beside the swimming pool,
Skeletons get on with life.
Skeletons are cool.

When everyone is feeling limp
Like overcooked spaghetti,
Skeletons get on with life.
Skeletons aren't sweaty.

They always look immaculate.
They always look so neat.
They always dress in bones, you see,
And bones don't overheat.

When temperatures are rocketing,
When dogs begin to drool,
Skeletons get on with life.
Skeletons are cool.

■ NO BONE UNTURNED

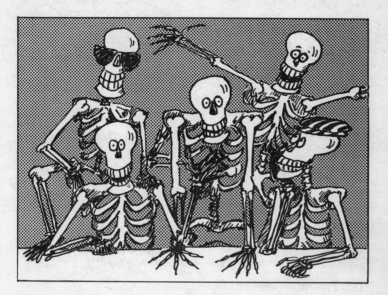

Exclusive Interview with Top Skeleton Pop Group

No Bone Unturned come from Gravesend. Their first single, 'Knit me a Rib Cardigan, Baby', sold thousands of copies (of the cardigan, not the record). They consist of:

Cool Keith – lead vocals, guitar
Tinkling Tall Trevor – keyboards, triangle
Leo Lanky – saxabone
Rattling Reg – drums
Big Bo Bonehead – bass guitar

Skeletons

Q. What's the first thing you do in the morning?

Cool Keith: I try and get myself together, man. I'm all to pieces in the morning.

T. T. Trevor: We all sleep in a pile, so it gets confusing.

Big Bo: Once I got Rattling Reg's head by mistake. It was totally empty.

Leo Lanky: And Trev and I ended up with each other's feet, didn't we, Trev? We're about the same size, you see. We went round like that for weeks.

Rattling Reg: What was the question again?

Q. What would you be if you weren't in a famous pop group?

Cool Keith: What, with my looks? A film star. Definitely. Don't I look great in these sun glasses?

Leo Lanky: A night watchman. You know, where they employ Skeleton staff.

Big Bo: A carpenter. Making coffins and them cupboards with inbuilt Skeletons that pop out. I'm good with my hands.

T. T. Trevor: I guess I'd just generally go round scaring people. Sounds boring, but the money's okay and you do get good holidays.

Rattling Reg: An umbrella stand. Or a brain surgeon. Something like that.

(Rest of group break up into uncontrollable laughter. Many hours later they finally get themselves sorted out and are able to continue with the interview.)

Q. What's the most horrible thing that's ever happened to you?

Cool Keith: Well, once I couldn't find my sunglasses . . .

T. T. Trevor: Breaking my ankle.

Leo Lanky: It wasn't *your* ankle. It was when we had each other's feet, remember? It was my ankle you broke, actually.

Big Bo: I hated having Reg's head most.

Rattling Reg: I didn't like having yours much either. Yours is a lot bigger than mine.

Q. Do you have any hints for other new Skeleton groups?

Cool Keith: Are you kidding? Why should we help them?

Leo Lanky: My advice is: don't go into the music business. Skeleton groups break up all the time.

T. T. Trevor: Most don't have the guts for it. You gotta be hard.

Big Bo: (*To Reg*) What d'you mean, my head's bigger than yours?

Rattling Reg: I'm fed up with answering questions. I want to play drums.

(They break into '**Knit Me a Rib Cardigan, Baby**')

Knit Me a Rib Cardigan, Baby

My baby has a way with wool,
Wool, wool, wool,
Her cardigans are wonderful,
Ful, ful, ful,
Purl and plain and plain and purl,
Purl, purl, purl,
What a knitter, what a girl!
Girl, girl, girl.

Chorus:
Oooh, oooh, Mary Anne,
Knit me a rib cardigan —
That is what I'd like a lot.
Baby, make them needles hot!

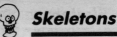

■ SKELETON INSULTS

If you wish to insult a skeleton, take your pick from the
following:

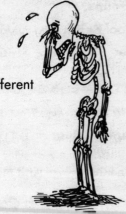

- 'You've got a cheek!'
- 'You've got a nerve!'
- 'Where are your guts?'
- 'I've seen your picture. You look different
  in the flesh.'
- 'You'll always be a nobody.'
- 'You're heartless.'
- 'I've got a bone to pick with you.'

■ JAW BREAKERS

Skeleton scouts show
exceptional skill in skunk
skinning.

Black bones, blue bones, big
brown brittle bones.

Rib tickle, rib tickle, like a
little rib tickle?

■ CLASSIFIED

JOBS

■ Cheerful Skeleton required by student doctor. Must be prepared to be dismantled, thrown around at parties and wrongly reassembled on a regular basis, so needs a sense of humour.

■ Fancy being snapped? Skeleton required to pose for photographs advertising the fabulous new Termite Formula crash diet. Must be prepared to smile while eating large quantities of dried termite spit.

■ Cleaning lady wanted. Must be prepared to work fingers to the bone and double as a hat stand when guests come to dinner. No wages but, if good worker, will be rewarded with boneus.

FLATS AND ROOMS

■ Small, cramped cupboard. Short let only. Resident Skeleton on holiday in cupboard in South of France.

■ GHOSTS ■ (IN STITCHES)

Howdy, Ghost readers. Craig Vague here. I'm having a wail of a time here at *Witches in Stitches* and hope you're going to enjoy reading your very own Ghost section. It's a real scream.

CONTENTS

■ LIMERICK

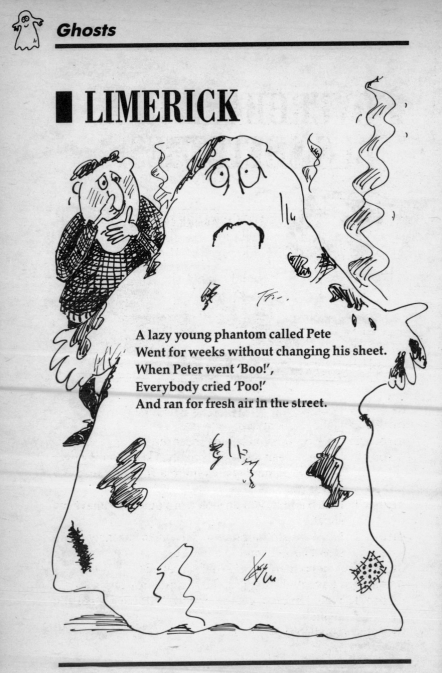

A lazy young phantom called Pete
Went for weeks without changing his sheet.
When Peter went 'Boo!',
Everybody cried 'Poo!'
And ran for fresh air in the street.

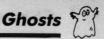

■ OVERHEARD IN A BUS SHELTER

GHOST 1: Wail, wail, wail. Fancy not seeing you!

GHOST 2: Hallo. Almost didn't see you.

GHOST 1: So. How are you booing these days?

GHOST 2: I haven't been too well, actually. I keep coming over all faint. Some days it's quite a fright to keep my spirits up.

GHOST 1: I must admit, you do look worn out. Look, have my sheet.

GHOST 2: No, I mustn't sit down. I'm off to the new chain store. I don't want to misty bus.

GHOST 1: A new chain store? What's it called?

GHOST 2: I haven't the foggiest. Here comes my bus.

GHOST 1: Wail, I'm off to get my air done. Nice to not see you again.

GHOST 2: Toodleboo.

■ POETRY CORNER

The Ghost in the Washing Machine

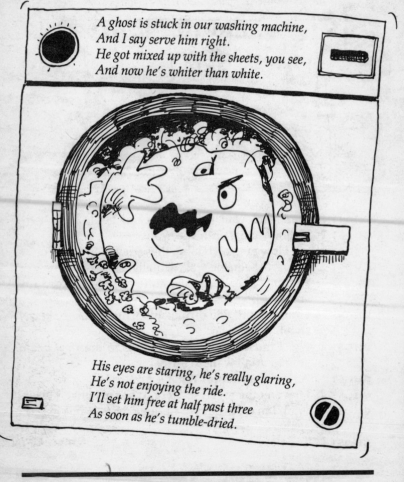

A ghost is stuck in our washing machine,
And I say serve him right.
He got mixed up with the sheets, you see,
And now he's whiter than white.

His eyes are staring, he's really glaring,
He's not enjoying the ride.
I'll set him free at half past three
As soon as he's tumble-dried.

The Elephantom

The Elephantom's big and white,
He haunts the local zoo.
The keepers say he comes at night
At one o'clock or two.

His tusks are sharp, his trunk is long,
His hide is tough and hairy.
He sings an Elephantom song –
Believe you me, he's scary.

He overturns the rubbish bins –
A shocking mess he makes.
He's looking for banana skins
And buns and sticky cakes.

The animals all shake with shock
And vainly try to hide.
They're glad their cage is safely locked
With them on the inside.

The Elephantom stomps around
Till three or maybe four,
Just chomping on the food he's found
In bins or on the floor.

And when the sun begins to rise,
He slukes his massive ears,
He waves his trunk and rolls his eyes –
Then simply disappears.

So now you know the truth about
Where all zoo rubbish goes,
Straight down the Elephantom's throat –
And then – who knows? Who knows?

■ HORRORSCOPES
by Terry Fying

Hairies

Be warned if you're considering buying something which could be classed as a status symbol – like a set of gold-plated chains or a designer suit of armour. Spending money on such luxuries will bring you bad luck. So there, swankpot.

Terrorus

You're thinking of redecorating your ruin or even moving, um I right? I'm not? You're not? So I'm wrong again. Who cares? Have an awful week.

Gremlini

Don't take any risks this week. Avoid floating under ladders, don't bring may blossom into your ruin, etc. That way you might stay out of trouble until Saturday when, according to the stars (which never lie), you're going to be sucked up by a vacuum cleaner along with a load of crumbs, dust, cat fur, hair combings and nail clippings. Think I'm talking a load of rubbish? I'm

telling you, it's in the bag. So will you be. Have a nice night.

Canscare

You are in a nostalgic mood. You keep returning to your old haunts and calling up old ghoul fiends, who say they can't see you because they're washing their air. Don't be too downhearted. Someone somewhere wants a miserable, tight-fisted, gargoyle-featured, moody, antisocial wet blanket like you. On second thoughts, have you ever considered becoming a hermit?

Leero

Here's some news to raise your spirits. You're going up in the world. Doors will open for you. You're about to be offered a new job with travel opportunities, high prospects and the possibility of a rise. In fact, the sky's the limit. Have you guessed what it is? Haunting the lift.

Virago

Venus rising on the cusp means that the changing moon will influence Jupiter rising, affecting the cycle of

Mercury, which in turn indicates that the third constellation will have an adverse effect on those of you born under this sign, culminating in you finding that you have terrible trouble understanding anything you read in magazines.

Scarepio

Do you want the good news or the bad news first? Sadly, your doctor has discovered that you are suffering from the dreaded Fading Disease, and in twenty-four hours you will no longer exist. The bad news is he forgot to tell you yesterday.

Saggyterribles

You Saggyterribles are keen types, but isn't it time you slowed down a bit? All that racing up and down dark corridors and all that enthusiastic wailing on battlements are likely to affect your health. Try taking it easy. Have a night off for a change. Relax. Put your sheet up and forget the ironing and the chain oiling. Whatever you planned to boo tonight, wait and boo it tomorrow.

Cutmecorn

Romance is in the air. You will meet a tall, very dead person wrapped in bandages. Yes, you've guessed it. You're going to fall in love with a

mummy. Forget it. Ghouls and mummys just don't get on. They spend all their time arguing about things. Graves versus pyramids. Sheets versus bandages. Such relationships always end very quickly. Remember the old saying? 'A ghoul and his mummy are soon parted.' It's true.

Aglarius

Great news for you, poor old Aglarians! At last Lady Luck has noticed you. You're going to inherit a ruined castle. At long last you can move out of your telephone box, throw away your rags and enjoy the life of a lord – hauntin', hootin' and hissin' – with plenty of good walls to walk through and invitations to all the best Ghost parties. Wait a minute. Just noticed a slight mistake in my calculations. That should read: you are NOT going to inherit a ruined castle. Oh, well. Back to the telephone box. Sorry about that.

Peskys

You little Peskys get on my nerves. All that stupid nonsense you go in for – tilting picture frames and making tables rise and things fly through the air. It's pathetic. Try doing a proper night's work down a dungeon for once. Stop playing at being supernatural. Then I might take you seriously enough to write you a proper horrorscope.

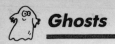

■ STORY

The Case of the Disappearing Head

Another classic from the casebook of Mick MacMenace, ghost detective.

It was one a.m. I was playing myself a game of draughts. I was losing. Losing at draughts really gets the wind up me. In fact, it had nearly come to blows. Luckily, the telephone rang.

'MacMenace here,' I drawled. That's me. Mick MacMenace, private eye. Weird and spooky happenings a speciality.

'Oh, Mr MacMenace. Thank goodness you're awake. This is Miss Misty, the secretary up at the Ghoul School. I'm terribly worried. The Head's head's gone missing.'

'Huh? How many heads did you say?'

'Just the one. The Head's.'

'Pity. Two heads are better than one. Heh, heh. Just kidding. Okay, I'll materialize right on over.'

I grabbed a clean sheet and ran a comb through my air. I like to take trouble with my appearance. Within seconds I was hovering before her, looking pretty cool, though I say it myself.

Miss Misty was one of those drab, faded types. I could see she was in a bit of a funk. She kept going fuzzy at the edges. She was dressed in one of those out-of-date Victorian outfits and kept dabbing at her eyes with a lace hanky.

'Okay, lady,' I said. 'What's the story?'

'It's Mr Dread, our headmaster. I was only out of the office for a few minutes, and when I came back that's how I found him.'

She pointed behind the desk. She was right. Dread's head was missing. His body was there all right, but above his neck – thin air. As I stared, the body waved its arms in a gesture of despair, leapt to its feet and immediately fell over the waste-paper basket.

'He can't see where he's going, poor man,' wept Miss Misty, as we got him back in the chair again. 'I keep telling him not to move, but he can't hear me, you see. Not without his ears. Oh, Mr MacMenace, what are we going to do? Mr Dread is such a kind, harmless man.'

'Armless? I thought he was headless,' I cracked. Just a little joke to cheer her up. 'Okay. Now, tell me. Is Dread the sort of guy who loses his head easily?'

'Oh, no, Mr MacMenace. He's very particular with it. He sends me out to buy shampoo for it, you know. And he's always trimming its beard. No, I'm quite sure he hasn't lost it through carelessness. He usually carries it under his arm. Sometimes he puts it on the desk. He's terribly attached to it. Well, he isn't at the moment, but you know what I mean. Only the other day he had its eyes tested and bought it a new pair of glasses. So it can see when he's writing reports. There they are,

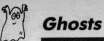

look. Oh, that wicked, wicked thief. At least he could have let it keep its glasses on.'

'No point,' I explained. 'It's sure to have been blindfolded. And gagged.'

'Oh, poor, poor Mr Dread!' sobbed Miss Misty and ran over to stroke Dread's body's hand. The body pushed her away irritably and turned its back on both of us. Obviously sulking.

I picked up the glasses and examined them. They were huge. Some Ghosts really like to make spectacles of themselves.

'Whoever would want to steal a head that doesn't belong to them?' cried Miss Misty.

'Some kinda nut nut, I guess,' I said. I like cracking nut jokes. 'Don't wring your hands like that, honey. I keep thinking it's the telephone. Heh, heh. No, seriously. If you wanna help your boss, I need some answers to a few questions. Who comes in here?'

'Everyone. In Mr Dread's office, it's an ever-open wall. The staff, the pupils, trans-parents, all trooping through day and night, always late for appointments . . .'

'Hold it. You said the staff. What staff?'

'Well, there's Miss Banshee, the music teacher. And Frank Enstein, he takes science with the top juniors. Then there's Mrs Jinx, she takes the slow wailers. Mr Moonmad, he takes the younger Werewolves, and Miss Spectre takes the general subjects – weeping, sheet care, walking through walls and so on.'

'Is that it?'

'Well, yes. Except for the dinner ladies, but they leave after lunch.'

'Can't say I blame 'em. I used to leave half my lunch when I was a kid. Get it? After lunch. Half dere lunch. Sound kinda similar when you say it quick, heh, heh. Anyone else?'

'Just Zack Zombie, our scaretaker.'

'Call 'em. I feel kinda irritable. I'll give 'em a cross-examination. Geddit? Irritable. *Cross*-examination . . .'

But Miss Misty wasn't listening. She collared this little Werewolf and asked him to take a message. He told her it was bay time and bit her hand. Nasty little nipper. I threw him a couple of lamb chops and finally he agreed. You have to know how to handle these kids.

One by one the staff drifted in clutching mugs of coffee. They were a ghastly-looking bunch. Typical teachers. They started off moaning a lot because they were missing their break, but fell silent when they saw the headless Dread propped forlornly on his chair. If ever a body looked depressed, that one did. Miss Misty patted his shoulder and tried pouring coffee down his neck. He choked. Everyone fell about laughing. Even Miss Misty. It was a real funny choke.

The last to arrive was Zack Zombie. I had a hunch about him. He had one too, on his left shoulder. Typical school scaretaker. Big, mean, poisoned spike in one hand and sack of confiscated footballs in the other.

'Is dis gonna take long?' he growled. 'I got work to do. Gotta puncture all these kids' footballs. Little so-and-sos keep kickin' 'em up in the gutterin'.'

'Siddown, Zombie,' I snapped. 'There's been a robbery. Your head's boss has gone missing. I mean your boss's head. Know anything about it?'

'Why should I? I'm a flesh-eating revived corpse. I ain't no tea leaf.'

Suddenly, there was a commotion. Dread was struggling to stand up, waving his arms around and pointing towards the sack of footballs Zombie held in his hand. He was obviously trying to tell me something . . .

Will Mick discover the secret of Zack Zombie's bag of footballs? Will Mr Dread get his head back in time to write the end-of-term reports? Is Miss Misty all she seems to be? Buy the next issue of *Witches in Stitches*, and read the next thrilling instalment!

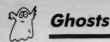
■ GHOST JOKES

- Where do Ghosts buy stamps?
  At the Ghost Office.
- Father Ghost:
  Spook when you're spoken to.
- What game do little Ghosts like playing most?
  Haunt the slipper.
- Who is the painted lady Ghost with the famous scowl?
  Moaner Lisa.

■ READERS' LETTERS

Write to: Sadie Shady,
Witches in Stitches.

Dear Sadie,

It's time the Ghost pages included a cookery column. Just to start you off, here is my dish of the week.

Phantom Splodge
1. Take the holes out of three Polos. Place in bowl.
2. Add ½ cup of mist.
3. Add a good pinch of air.
4. Whisk.
5. Scoff.

Spooky Sukie, Brighton

● *This is thoroughly delicious, particularly when eaten with a large tin of rice pudding.*

Dear Sadie,

I was furious to read a letter from a reader saying suits of armour are old-fashioned and look ridiculous.

I've been wearing the same suit since 1688. I got it mail order. It irons beautifully. I wonder what your reader's nylon sheet will look like in three hundred years?

Rusty Greaves, Grimsby

● *Trendier than your armour.*

Dear Sadie,

Armour is real heavy, OK?

Hippy Ghost

P.S. Ice is cool. A low tide is far out. Records are groovy.

● *A hat is right on. You are mad.*

Dear Sadie,

Young ghosts these days have no musical taste. Just look at all those awful pop groups they watch on *Shriek of the Week,* that disgraceful television programme. I have to stuff up my ears whenever it's on. Whatever happened to the beautiful haunting melodies of yesterday? The sort of tunes that one sings in the bath?

The Phantom of the Opera

● *In the bath? Are you talking about soap operas? They sank without trace.*

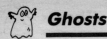

■ CLASSIFIED

ITEMS FOR SALE

■ Wardrobe Clearance
Pile of assorted sheets. Hardly worn. Reasonably clean, eye holes already cut. Owner feels the cold, gone over to duvets.

■ Suit of Armour
Ever felt you needed something smart for that special occasion? Now's your chance. Full suit of armour, incuding gauntlets, greaves, etc. Oil-can thrown in free. Incredibly uncomfortable, but looks flash. Swank while you clank, and be the envy of all your friends.

■ Moany Walkman
Hardly used. Ideal for ghosts with a musical ear. Comes with a selection of tapes, including wailing, screaming, crazed laughing, etc. Fed up with drifting along dark corridors feeling bored? Just plug in and waft along to the latest sounds! Makes haunting less daunting.

■ Head Bag
A great new idea! Specially designed bags for those of you who get tired of walking around with your head tucked underneath your arm. These light, nylon bags are fully lined for maximum comfort, and have cleverly placed peep-holes so you can see where you're going! A choice of three colours – blood-red, misty grey or white. At last, a chance to stretch your arm without losing your head.

■ Pain-free Chains
Fed up with dragging around in those heavy, rusty chains which bite into your ankles? Try the latest in fashionable ankle wear. Pain-free chains, light but noisy, specially designed to prevent chafing. A combination of plastic and elastic, these chains look like the real thing, rattle like the real thing – but they're a joy to wear. Your closest fiends won't be able to tell the difference and will think you're suffering as usual, so you'll still get plenty of sympathy.

■ Invisible Ink
100,000,000,000 bottles of invisible ink going cheap. You can't see it but, trust me, it's there. No, really.

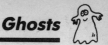

DRIPPY'S DUNGEON SALE!

YES! FOR THREE WEEKS ONLY, DRIPPY'S, THE NUMBER 1
DUNGEON SPECIALISTS, ARE PREPARED TO FULLY FIT
YOUR DUNGEON AT ⅓ OF THEIR USUAL PRICE!

Drippy's do **everything**, from installing top-quality dripping walls (in a
choice of tasteful greens) to getting the echo just right.
Now it's better value than ever, with a free personal design service and
free accessories, including NOOSE, LARGE BUNCH OF KEYS,
your very own SKELETON and, of course, your FREE FULL-
COLOUR BROCHURE. Ideal for the kind of ghost who does a lot of
entertaining and wants to show off.

EXCITING RANGE ★ DISGUSTING PUDDLES ★ FETID
SMELLS ★ DRY ROT ★ WET ROT ★ DEATH WATCH
BEETLE ★ RATS ★ SPIDERS ★ COCKROACHES ★ RUSTY
TORTURE INSTRUMENTS ★ SUSPICIOUS RED STAINS
ON FLOOR ★ EASY PAYMENT PLAN ★ FULL
GUARANTEE

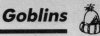

■ GOBLINS ■
(IN STITCHES)

i am ron clot. i am a goblin editer. i am reel stoopid. i can hold a pencil. just.

CONTENTS

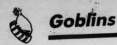
■ LIMERICK

A silly young Goblin named Crumpet
Decided he'd like to play trumpet.
A trumpet, you know,
Works fine if you blow,
But not, if like Crumpet, you thump it.

GOBLIN JOKES

- How do you get a Goblin to stop biting his nails?
  Put mustard on his boots.
- What do you call an intelligent Goblin?
  An imposter.
- Why do Goblins wear their bobble hats pulled down over their eyes?
  To protect their foreheads when they bump into trees.
- What about the Goblin who went to the mind reader?
  He got his money back.
- How do you recognize a Goblin aeroplane?
  It has outside toilets.
- Why did the Goblin go to the dentist?
  To have a wisdom tooth put in.

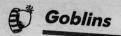

POETRY CORNER

The Problem

The Goblin had a problem.
He invariably put
The left boot on the wrong way round
(The right on the wrong foot).
He thought he had the problem licked,
He thought he had it beat:
He marked each boot with LEFT and RIGHT –
But failed to mark his feet!

Rhyming Poem by Anon

Writing poems ain't no joke,
It's hard to make 'em rhyme.
You think and think and think and think,
It is a waste of . . . .
. . . . ?? . . . . ??? . . . .
. . . . ?? . . . . money.

A Goblin's Really Thick

A Goblin's brain is like a drain,
I'm very sad to say.
When Goblins think, it's like a sink
When water flows away.
A tortoise, by comparison,
Is really very quick:
To put it in a nutshell, kids –
A Goblin's really thick.

He Jumps out of Bed

He jumps out of bed in the morning,
It's quite a long way to drop.
He doesn't recall (till he starts to fall)
That he sleeps in the bunk on the top.

He goes out the door in the afternoon
As merrily as can be.
He doesn't recall (till he starts to fall)
That his house is built in a tree.

He goes for a walk after teatime,
The evening air to sniff.
He doesn't recall (till he starts to fall)
That the road stops dead at the cliff.

It takes him a while to get home again
(With the cliff and the tree to climb).
He crawls into bed with a terrible head –
And then it's morning time, SO . . .

He jumps out of bed in the morning . . . etc.

DESIGNER BADGES!

EXCLUSIVE OFFER!
THESE DELIGHTFUL BADGES CAN BE YOURS.
LIMITED OFFER.
COLLECTOR'S ITEMS £1 FOR SIX.
10 PENCE FOR SEVEN!

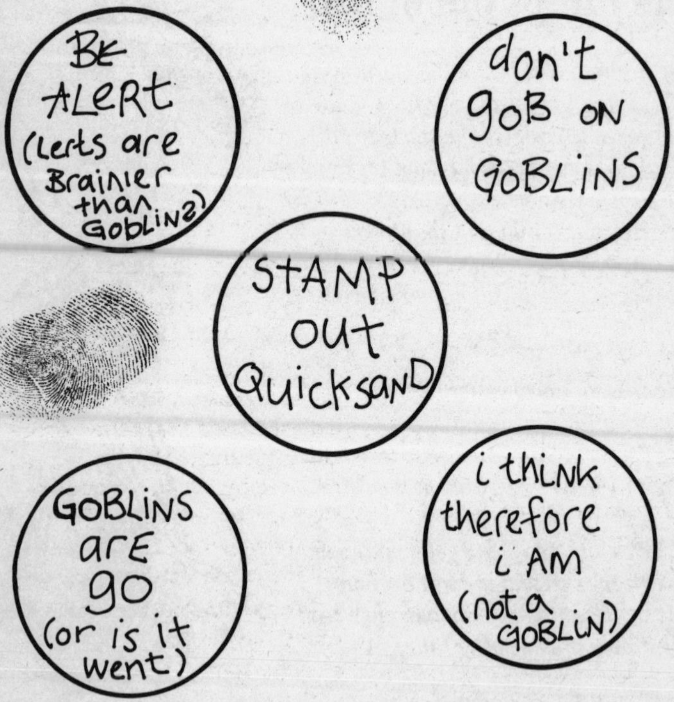

▮ ETIQUETTE

Table Manners

• Never rest your elbows on the table. Place them neatly in the dinners of the Goblins on either side of you. If they object, place your fists neatly in their mouths.

• Never ask if you may leave the table. Take it with you.

• Always bolt your food. You might lose your appetite before you've finished.

• If your neighbour chokes over his food, bang him on the back. If he chokes over yours, bang him in the eye.

• A spoon is provided for the sole purpose of flicking lumps of custard into your neighbour's eye. A fork is for sticking in his leg. A knife is for cleaning wax out of your ears and/or cutting your toenails. On no account use these implements for eating. What do you think your fingers are for?

When to say 'Please' and 'Thank you'

These archaic words have almost passed out of the Goblin language and have been replaced by the more popular kicking, snatching, etc. They can, however, be used in the following dire emergencies:

• When someone has you round the throat.

• When a twelve-foot monster with three heads is passing chocolate around.

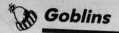

■ A DAY IN THE LIFE OF A GOBLIN by Sid Squalid

8.30 My little sister Maggot thumps me with a mallet and sets fire to my pyjamas. Ho-hum. Another day. Time to get up.

8.31 Put Maggot and pyjamas in bucket of water. Get dressed. Put on boots first. Look for socks in drawer. One red, one blue. Very unusual. Got another pair like that. Put socks over boots. Something wrong somewhere. Must be the other way round. Start again. Socks first, then boots. That's better. Tie laces. Fall over. Must remember to take smaller steps. Shirt next. Must get wrists pierced so I can wear new cufflinks. Finally, bobble hat. That's me dressed. Oops. Not quite. Forgot trousers. Trousers won't go on over boots. Start again . . .

10.30 Finish getting dressed. Go down to breakfast. Charred boiled eggs again. Our mum in bad mood. Our pet tiger Spot has eaten her green wig, dad's sandwiches, Maggot's tricycle and last month's left-over stew what was supposed to be for tea. He don't look too good. No one does after our mum's stew.

10.45 Dad goes to work. He's got a job blowing up balloons for the Goblin Space Programme. They're working on putting a Goblin on the sun. Dad says he won't get frazzled to a crisp like what you might think because they're sending him at night.

11.00 Dad comes running in shouting that the steering wheel, the gear lever, the brake and the accelerator of the car have all been stolen. He got into the back seat by mistake. He's always doing that.

11.15 Time for exercises. Jump up and down on spot. He bites my ankle. Must be feeling better.

11.30 Put Elastoplast on boot.

11.45 Get two-piece jigsaw puzzle out. Been working on it for months. Determined to crack it today.

12.00 After lot of thought, realize what problem is. One piece missing. Spot looks guilty.

12.30 Lunchtime. Salt and pepper in warmed-up water again. Mum economizing.

12.45 Spot throws up Maggot's tricycle. The bell doesn't work. Maggot in temper. Sets fire to her home arsonist kit, Spot's basket and the kitchen. Mum sends her to play outside in the quicksand.

1.00 Decide to spring-clean room. Try ironing curtains. Fall out of window. Luckily, ground breaks my fall.

1.30 Go out and look for fight.

2.00 Have one with Bruiser Baggins. Lose. Come home. Think I'll stay in and beat myself up tomorrow. It doesn't hurt so much.

3.00 Decide to paint room. Tin says put on two coats. Get much too hot. Stop painting room. Iron socks. Burn feet.

3.15 Brick smashes through window with message attached. It says, 'I Am Yore Noo Postman'. Why don't Goblins have a proper postal service like everyone else?

3.16 Another brick, from Bruiser Baggins. It says, 'Go Hom Sid.' I am home. Is he mad?

3.30 Practise tap dancing. Fall in sink.

4.0 Spot throws up stew. Green wig and sandwiches still down there somewhere. Mum pokes down his throat with mop handle, but no luck.

5.0 Teatime. Stew. Funny, I didn't see her cooking today . . .

6.0 Go to pictures to see *Goblin Hood and his Merry Bunch of Idiots*. Can't get in. Some bloke keeps tearing my ticket in half.

7.0 Come home. Watch telly. Wish it was working. Maggot wants me to play with her. We take turns at hitting each other with mallet. For some reason, develop slight headache. Think I'll have an early night.

7.30 Go to bed. Pyjamas rather uncomfortable, being burnt to a frazzle and soaking wet. Put them on over clothes, so they're not next to skin. Keep snoring and waking myself up. Go to sleep in spare room. Much better.

8.0 Spot throws up wig on my bed. Mum'll be pleased. Only the sandwiches to go. Zzzzzzzzzzzzz.

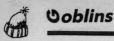

YOU TOO CAN FIND LOVE

GOBOLOVE introductions have been the start of romance for many thousands of Goblins. Our clients all have two things in common:

1 They want to meet a Goblin with the same hopes, ambitions, boot size and taste in bobble hats as themselves.
2 They're stupid.

Gobolove is the **largest** dating agency in the universe, ensuring that there are more idiots for you to meet.

Our unique matching system guarantees that you are mutually compatible. When you join **Gobolove, you choose** the sort of Goblin you would like to meet by completing our questionnaire.

Gobolove is **not expensive.** A year's membership is an investment in your future happiness, so stop carping about having to sell your house, your clothes and your tricycle, you ungrateful little nerd.

Hobnail and Grizzle

Grizzle's family thought she was an idiot to join Gobolove. She was ugly enough to get any Goblin she wanted. Hobnail had met lots of girl Goblins interested in the glamour of his uniform (he's an active memer of the G F S S – Goblin Fly-swatting Squad). But both he and Grizzle hoped to meet someone wanting the same things out of life – food, fighting and ferret-rearing. Grizzle says, 'I'd been looking for someone special. Hobnail has everything. Dirty fingernails, matted hair, terrible table manners, a way with ferrets and pots of money.' Hobnail says, 'Grizzle's the girl for me. Ever seen such a mess?'

Hobnail and Grizzle married two days after Gobolove introduced them and are now running a ferret farm! If you want to find true love like this happy couple, complete this test and post it today!

Computer test to find your ideal goblin

Please send me a description of my ideal Goblin. I enclose my life's savings.

1 Level of Stupidity

Do you consider yourself to be:

☐ Rather stupid
☐ Stupid
☐ Of average stupidity
☐ Very stupid
☐ Utterly stupid
☐ Fantastically stupid
☐ Unbelievably stupid
☐ Colossally stupid
☐ Mindbogglingly stupid

2 Fashion

Do you think you look like:

☐ A tramp
☐ A clown
☐ A wally
☐ Something that's crawled from under a stone
☐ A piece of cheese

3 Activities and interests

Do you enjoy:

☐ Goblin music
☐ Bullying little fluffy things
☐ Feeding your face
☐ Picking your pimples

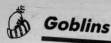

■ A LETTER

deer wiches in stiches

im juss ritin ter sa dat im sik
uv peepul ~~riddt ridbc riddicool~~ takin
de mikky outer us goblins, makin out
we is fick an all dat, oo sez we aint
got no brayns yer well alrite evrywon,
but I dote fink iss fare, me an my
goblin maytes is gettin rite cheezed orf
wot wiv peeple sayin we is ugli an smelli
an carnt spel, so aniway wot i sa is
dis com on all yoo goblins let us fite bak,
iss time we got sum good pres wot sq yoo,
let us all rite to de noospappers reelly
~~intely inte lttij intalergent~~ braney
leters lik dis won wot i am ritin and
den we wil get a repootayshun for
been jeanyusses wich is ~~oty~~ only rite
aint it?
M.T. BONCE
(Pressydent orve S.O.B.G - Society orve.
                    Braney Goblins)

*OUR FOUNDERS\$

Sossiety Orve Braney Goblins

Half a mind to join the SOBG? Well, half a mind's all you need. Most of our members don't even have that!

There will be a meeting in the telephone box when the big hand is on the twelve and the little hand is on the four (3 o'clock).

If wet, the meeting will take place outside.

In the unlikely event that more Braney Goblins turn up than can fit into a telephone box, don't worry. There was another meeting yesterday – you could have come to that.

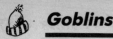

■ INTELLIGENCE TEST

Important. Do not answer more than **eleven** of these **six** questions. The correct answers are on page **96**.

Name _____

Address _____

NOTE: Those without address may draw their trousers in the space provided.

1 Count to five. What is the last number you reached?

   _____

2 Take four from two. What do you get?

   _____

3 Here is an answer. NO. What is the question?

   _____

4 Here is a list. Which is the odd one out?
   Goblin   Goblin   Goblin
   Goblin   Hippopotamus   Goblin

   _____

5 Can you do this Goblin Maze?

IN _____ OUT

6 What is different about these circles?

☐   ☐   ☐   ☐

_____

7 How do you spell INCORRECTLY?

_____

8 Join the dots and see what shape you get.

·1   ·2   ·3   ·4

9 Make three words out of the word GOBLIN.

_____

10 Spot ten differences between these two pictures:

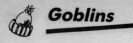
Answers

1 Eh?

2 A headache.

3 Did you get the answer right?

4 Goblin. All Goblins are odd.

5

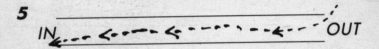

IN ⟵ ⟵ ⟵ ⟵ ⟵ OUT

6 What circles? I can only see triangles. Obviously a trick question.

7 EESILY

8

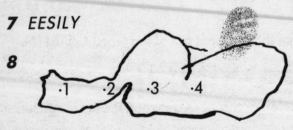

9 lgoibn, nlgiob, glnobi.

10 Another trick question. These pictures are identical.

◼ CROSSWORD PUZZLE

COMPETITION! Fill in the Crossword Puzzle, and WIN £1,000!

For those of you who can't wait, the solution is here.

Across

1. A squat, ugly creature with no brains.
2. Another one, facing backwards.

Down

1. Another one.
2. Another one, standing on his head.

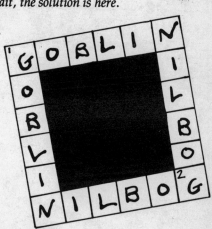

◼ CLASSIFIED

FOR SALE AND WANTED

- **For sale**: nearly-new rubber gloves. Wash your hands without getting them wet!
- **Wanted**: cap with peak at back.

- **For sale**: Goblin-designed parachute. Opens on impact.
- **For sale**: 1,000 sheets sandpaper. When fitted together, make interesting map of Sahara Desert.
- **Wanted**: Peep-toed bovver boots. I'm going on holiday.

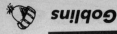

all **25** for ownli **4p** each + P&P

CLEVER GOBLIN SAYINGS
Philippa Postage-stamp

Bobble hAT BUK club

Rosa NeTTLes

M.T. PAGE

MORE CLEVER GOBLIN SAYINGS

GOBLIN GARDENING

GOBLIN HABITS
R.E. VOLTING

Send 7 million £3 pues NoW To us OR ELse . . . . .

Name ————
Adres s ————

THE REST OF ■ A BAD BUNCH ■ (IN STITCHES)

Hello there, boys and girls. Aunty Sandy here. This section's for all the rest of you monsters, so that you don't feel left out. There was a lot of competition for this job, but finally, much to my delight, they decided that Mummy always knows best. Happy reading!

CONTENTS

■ LIMERICK

The rest of the monsters felt blue:
'Hey! We buy this magazine too!
Some pages for us, or we'll
Make quite a fuss!'
Okay, then. This section's for you.

■ MONSTER JOKES

How do you get fur from a werewolf?
Get as fur away as you can.

What do you get if you cross a large gorilla with a strawberry icecream?
King Kone.

. . . Or a large gorilla with a chestnut?
King Konker.

FIRST ZOMBIE: Oops, my arm's dropped off, just below the elbow.
SECOND ZOMBIE: Don't worry, I'll give you a hand.
FIRST ZOMBIE: But it's the wrist of it I'm worried about.

The Mummy's motto: If at first you don't deep-freeze, dry, dry, dry again.

▌POETRY CORNER

My Father is a Werewolf

My father is a werewolf.
Right now he's busy moulting.
He leaves his hairs on stairs and chairs –
It's really quite revolting.
And if my friends make comments
(For some of them are faddy),
I tell them it's the cat or dog.
I never say it's Daddy.

My Mummy

My Mummy is a Mummy,
She's very tightly wrapped,
And if I touch her bandages,
I get my fingers slapped.

■ SAFETY

How to avoid being attacked by a Werewolf

Try any of the following methods:

1 Tap lightly over the nose with a rolled up newspaper, yelling, 'Sit!' in your firmest voice. Then run.

2 Waggle a lead around in a tempting manner, saying, 'Walkies?' If you succeed in gaining its trust, make briskly for nearest quicksand.

3 Approach in friendly fashion, wave a poisoned Jaffa cake under its nose, and say, 'Nice bikky?'

4 Point to a bucket of paint stripper and say, 'Does 'oo want oo's din-dins den?' in sugary voice.

5 Encourage it to accompany you to a very high cliff, throw a stick and shout, 'Fetch!'

6 If firmer tactics are needed, try threatening it with obedience classes/the vet/Battersea Dogs' Home/flea spray/a bath/next door's Doberman Pinscher.

7 Be kind. It might be lonely. Try taking it to the zoo. If it gets bored, try the pictures.

8 Keep it as a pet. Build it a kennel. Give it a basket in front of the fire. Slip it scraps under the table. Let it sleep on your bed. Make it feel wanted and part of the family. (Suggest you first discuss this plan with your parents.)

If readers have any further suggestions, please send them to:
Witches in Stitches, Werewolf Department, Sinister House, Transylvania
Note: If full moon, don't expect a reply.

■ PEN PALS

■ Hi! My name is Betty, and I'm a Yeti. I can't be bothered to write letters, but would like to meet anyone interested in howling on mountains. I'll be outside the cinema at eight tomorrow. I'm four metres tall, covered in matted hair, and my knuckles brush the ground when I walk. I'll wear a pink carnation so you'll recognize me.

■ Hi! My name is Embalma Shrivel. I'm a Mummy, and I'd like to correspond with a Sugar Deady. My hobbies include bathing in embalming fluid and giving bandage demonstrations for the Red Cross. Please write to: *Embalma Shrivel, 1, Nile View, Pyramid Estate, The Desert, Egypt*

■ Och ay the noo! I'm Nessy, and I'd like to write to anyone interested in water sports. If that good-looking shark from *Jaws* is reading this, perhaps he'd like to get in touch? I've got a bubbly personality and have an interesting job terrifying tourists. Why don't you drop me a wee line? I promise you, I'm quite a catch. Please write to: *Nessy, Loch Ness, Scotland*

■ Hi! Frankenstein's monster here. I'm tall, with rather an unusual bolt through my neck, which gives me a magnetic appeal. Household appliances find me irresistible. Female vacuum cleaners are always trying to suck up to me, and traffic lights wink as I stroll by. I'm into very fast music, and my ambition is to be a lightning conductor. Please write to me c/o: *Dr Frankenstein, Doom House, Storm-on-the-Wold*

■ Hi dear sirs. I beg your pardon for that bother you. I am a Troll in Norway. For work, I am a policeman. I have my own patroll car. My hobby is the rock music. I am so pleased to trouble you. I should like to turn to you with an ask. I have liking for a pen pal. I think you can make me this little help. A pen pal would be grand joy for me. We will write in the English. I think you will appreciate what I am saying and if this pal of the pen will write I him two will. Wilco, how you say, over and out. Please me to write: *P. C. Rocky Stone, Denkjenteknutkust-forlagprekstjorden, Norway*

WIN!

TEN LIFE-SIZE MONSTER MODELS!

Yes! From next month these cute, life-size monsters will be available in gift shops all over the country. And *Witches in Stitches* has TEN of these wonderful models to give away! Just send in your answers to the following questions on a postcard.

1 Are Werewolves snappy dressers?

2 Is a cycle-ops a one-eyed giant on a motorbike?

3 Is a flying sorcerer a mug?

4 Is a blood-drinking sheep a Lambpire?

5 What kind of loon would even **want** ten life-size monster models?

Complete this sentence in under ten words:

I am the kind of loon who would love to win ten life-size

monster models because _____

_____

■ MONSTER LIFESTYLES

Many Monsters are rather reclusive and don't like publicity. However, our intrepid reporter has tracked some of them down to bring you these exclusive interviews!

Abominable Snowman (Yeti)

A tall, furry, human-like creature that prowls the mountaintops by night looking for yaks (shaggy, ox-like animals which are a Yeti delicacy, unfortunately for them). No Abominable Snowman has ever been captured or photographed, although huge footprints have been seen in the snow. However, they do exist. Just ask a yak.

Image Big, butch and shaggy. We don't wear clothes. We've got our fur to keep us warm.

Hang-out Caves or shacks in the Himalaya Mountains.

Favourite food Yaks, mainly. But we prefer mountain climbers. No horns to stick in your throat. Also we pinch their macintoshes, backpacks and sacks of food. And their flags.

Likes Shacks, yaks, macs, backpacks, sacks, Union Jacks and leaving tracks. Oh, and kicking snow in people's faces.

Dislikes Wasting time talking to reporters when we could be out hunting yaks or mountaineers.

Illnesses Chilblains.

Remedy Boots. Some hope. Seen the size of our feet?

Greatest desire To meet an Abominable Snowwoman. You don't know of one, do you? And to find a pair of snow shoes big enough to fit.

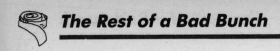

Banshee

Female spirit whose wailing foretells the deaths of members of noble Irish families.

Image Tear-stained. Torn, muddy gowns. That sort of thing.

Hang-out Irish bogs, to be sure.

Favourite food Scream of tomato soup.

Likes Sobbing, wailing, howling, moaning, screeching, tearing our hair in grief and generally making one heck of a racket.

Dislikes Being told to shut up.

Illnesses Sore throats.

Remedy Gargling and woolly scarves.

Greatest desire To form a pop group.

Cyclops

A giant with one eye in the centre of its forehead. A famous Greek sailor named Odysseus tricked the Cyclops by doing something rather nasty to his eye and escaped by clinging to a sheep's stomach. A pleasant little tale to read at bedtime.

Image Personally, I go for the casual look. Sheepskin jacket and rope sandals. Set off by matching accessories, like a knobbly club with nails in it. And a bone through the nose.

Hang-out Caves in Ancient Greece.

Favourite food Greeks. Especially if they're called Odysseus.

Likes Sheep. And eating Greeks. Especially if they're called Odysseus.

Dislikes Greeks called Odysseus. And the fact that they only sell contact lenses in pairs.

Illnesses Eye strain.

Remedy Spectacles, but they look stupid. And, like I said, no one'll sell you a single contact lens. Somebody ought to complain.

Greatest desire To spend five minutes – just five minutes, that's all – up a dark alley with Odysseus.

Dragon

Enormous, fire-breathing reptile known in legends throughout the world. Sometimes came with a set of wings. Fond of collecting treasure. People would often sacrifice a spare princess in order to have a quiet life.

Image Kind of slinky. Most of us have rather attractive scales which come in several shades of green.

Hang-out Caves. Preferably in volcanoes.

Favourite food Red-hot coals in ash sauce. Washed down with a nice cup of lava. I like a nice curried princess, of course, when I can get one.

Likes Ravaging, pillaging, nicking treasure, bullying princesses, fighting knights, eating Indian take-away.

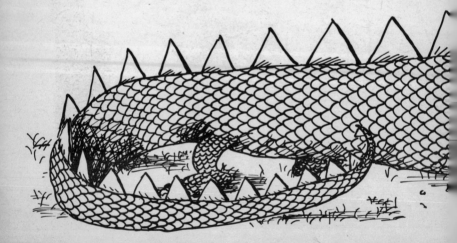

Dislikes People who say we're extinct. And swank-pots called St George, who think they know everything.

Illnesses Scorched tongues. High temperatures. Hot flushes. That sort of thing.

Remedy Those white pills you get from the vet. I think they're called snowballs. Three after meals, and you're fine.

Greatest desire To meet Princess Diana.

Loch Ness Monster

A famous monster who inhabits Loch Ness, a lake in northern Scotland. Many people claim to have seen the creature, and a number have taken photographs, none of which are very clear. A big tourist attraction.

Image I spend most of my time underwater, so there's not much call to dress up. I go in for straight scales. Those photographs you see are most unflattering. They don't look like me at all.

Hang-out Murky Scottish pond.

Favourite food Fish. Egg rolls left by tourists. I had a Marks and Spencer frozen pizza once. That was nice.

Likes Taking the micky out of tourists. Synchronized swimming except I haven't got anyone to do it with. Individual fruit pies, especially gooseberry.

Dislikes Being bombarded with empty Coke tins and pointed at and photographed every time I pop up for air.

Illnesses Indigestion. Comes from eating too much junk food.

Remedy To ignore all the rubbish the picnickers leave and stick to a light, sensible diet. But I just can't resist those little trifles that come from Sainsbury's . . .

Greatest desire To have something truthful written about me in the papers for once. And for someone to take a flattering photo, with proper studio lighting.

Troll

Huge, burly creature with a body formed out of mountain rock. Extremely dirty – often so filthy that plants and moss grow on it. Rather stupid and easily tricked. If it can be prevented from getting back to its cave before sunrise, it turns into a lifeless lump of stone.

Image Exceedingly filthy. We Trolls are individualists. Me, I have this small pine tree growing from my head. My roots are always growing out, but it looks trendy, yah?

Hang-out The high lumps of Norway. You call them mountains, yah?

Favourite food I am liking Norwegian sausage and the sticks of rock. Granite-flavoured, if you please.

Likes I am oh so loving the stomping around so covered with dirt that the pretty little flowers and moss grow on me, you know? We Trolls wear a sign. It is saying, 'Don't Clean Me, Plant Something.' Is good, uh?

Dislikes Is difficult question. Soap. Black and Decker hedge trimmers.

Illnesses If you have the plants growing on you, you must be expecting the little bit of skin trouble.

Remedy Slug pellets. And daily spray with insecticide.

Greatest desire I am in very need of digital watch. This will be of great benefit to me. I will get back to my cave by sunrise and will not be turning into a lump of lifeless stone, which can ruin social life.

Mummy

A body embalmed for burial. Ancient Egyptians believed that if they were well wrapped up, they'd reach the afterlife in one piece. They made sure that all their favourite things (jewels, cameras, hi-fi, etc.) were buried with them, as they didn't want to go to the expense of replacing them when they reached the Other Side. They also took along a packed lunch in case they got peckish.

Image Good old-fashioned bandages, that's what I like. Simple, neat, and you don't have to bother with underwear.

Hang-out Pyramids in Ancient Egypt.

Favourite food Chicken in a casket.

Likes I do enjoy a good joke. Especially if it's about sand. I've got this dry sense of humour. Here's a joke I heard the other day.
I am a Pharaoh. My name is Nuff. Pharaoh Nuff.
Ha ha ha.

Dislikes Tomb robbers. It's a terrible area for it. I've been robbed so many times they won't renew my pyramid insurance. They've taken everything worth having. My crown, my model camel collection, my signed photo of Cleopatra – even the banana sandwiches I was saving for the afterlife.

Illnesses I suffer from sar-cough-agus throat, which means I get this dry cough now and then.

Remedy I always make sure I'm well wrapped up.

Greatest desire To have a good scratch. That's the only disadvantage with these bandages. There's this spot between my shoulder blades – would you mind just . . . ? There ⁚ . . No, a bit more to the right . . . Aaaaah. Lovely.

Werewolf

A human who takes on the form of a wolf and prowls the night searching for people to attack. Can only be killed by a weapon made of silver.

Image Depends on what time it is. I'm one of those types who look totally different when they go out. Sort of like Batman.

Hang-out Anywhere, really. As long as it's full moon.

Favourite food Raw person. Chump chops. Rare steak. Mince, at a push.

Likes Having a cosy night in, watching *The Jungle Book* on video. You know how it is. Sometimes I just can't be bothered to change.

Dislikes Shaving. It takes hours. And going to the vet.

Illnesses Distemper. Thorns in the paw. I feel a little were-y now and then.

Remedy Moping in my basket for a week, then being dragged into the vet's waiting-room, where I'm stared at by cats for hours and then finally given a course of injections which costs the earth.

Greatest desire To meet Mowgli. And to learn the trick of shampooing my face without getting soap in my eyes.

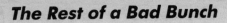

■ MUSIC PAGE

Monsterpoll Top 10

1 *The Skeleton Stomp*
Bononoroma (Bone Records)

2 *Nobody Loves Me*
Harry Tosis and the Bad Teeth (Stinkeroo)

3 *Knit Me a Rib Cardigan Baby*
No Bone Unturned (Bone Records)

4 *The Funky Mummy*
Ken Krumbly and the Desiccations (Embalma)

5 *Gimmee the Moonlight*
Slaverin' Stevens (Moontown)

6 *Who's That Monster?*
Mad Donna (Loonytoon)

7 *Giant Hits*
Talbot Trendy (BIG)

8 *Let There Be Rock*
Chip Stone and the Pebbles (Troll)

9 *You'll Never Squawk Alone*
Screaming Banshees (Caterwaul)

10 *The Yeti Shuffle*
Brett Sweaty (Snowman Sounds)

Chart compiled by Monsterpoll. Listen to your favourite hits every Sunday (5–7 p.m.) on Radio Monster.

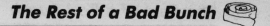
THE SCREAMING BANSHEES

SPECIAL EDITION
DOUBLE ALBUM

including the hit singles

Bawling Matilda (12″ remix)
Poor Jenny Sits A-shrieking (12″)
We'll Shriek Again (12″)
I Lost My Voice in San Francisco (12″)
You'll Never Squawk Alone (12″)

ONE HUNDRED AND TWENTY-THREE

■ THE MONSTER ALPHABET

A *is for* **AAAAAAAAAAAARGH!** A pleasant, informal greeting uttered by human beings when first introduced.

B *is for* **Banshee** A charming young woman with exceptional musical talent.

C *is for* **Creepy Crawlies** Delightful little creatures which can either be kept as pets or cooked, according to preference.

D *is for* **Dracula** A well-loved, highly suckcessful media personality. Used to be a film star but now a little too long in the tooth.

E *is for* **EEEEEEEEEEEEK!** Alternative informal greeting uttered by human beings when first introduced.

F *is for* **Fungus** Squidgy sort of mouldy growth, often found on top of old rice pudding. When scraped off, can be served as a side salad.

G *is for* **Ghost** Dim type, usually found queueing up outside shops offering cut-price sheets.

H *is for* **Hallowe'en** Popular inter-monster punch up. A fun night for all the family.

I *is for* **Illusion** Descriptive term applied to a Lusion who's not feeling well. (See **L** for Lusion.)

J *is for* **Jaws** Kindly man-eating shark who loves children.

K *is for* **King Kong** A misunderstood gorilla who'll do anything for a twenty-metre banana.

L *is for* **Lusion** Small, sickly, gnome-like creature, so thoroughly extinct that it probably only existed long enough for someone to make a joke about its name (see **I**).

M *is for* **Mummy** Sometimes married to Deady.

N *is for* **Nightmare** Human term for a beautiful dream about monsters.

O *is for* **Ogre** Fun-loving, man-eating giant, often unjustly criticized by newspaper reporters — particularly if they're in the process of being eaten at the time.

P *is for* **Poltergeist** A mischievous Ghost. Not to be confused with a poultrygeist, which is a mischievous chicken.

Q *is for* **Queen Kong** Gorilla who stands on the Empire State Building wearing a dress and a tiara.

R *is for* **Ruin** Desirable property.

S *is for* **Skeleton** A person with the skin taken off.

T *is for* **Troll** Large Scandinavian monster who can't speak English properly. Totally mad as a rule. Hence the expression 'Off his/her trolly'.

U *is for* **UFO** In English-speaking countries, a UFO means a flying saucer. In China it stands for Unidentified Frying Object and generally means something nasty in a wok.

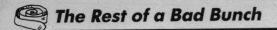

V *is for* **Vampire** A posh sort of monster, faddy about its diet (hates stakes, won't touch garlic, etc.). More likely to be found in a castle than a bungalow. See **D** for Dracula.

W *is for* **Werewolf** A split personality. Known as Derek by day, Bonzo by moonlight.

X *is for* **X-ray** Special sort of photograph. Invented by a Skeleton who was tired of seeing people in the flesh.

Y *is for* **Yeti** Alternative name for Abominable Snowman. Its footprints are rarely found, mainly because it can't get boots to fit. Well, would *you* stomp around barefoot in the snow if you could help it?

Z *is for* **Zombie** Scruffy revived corpse with glazed eyes. Tends to be a wallflower at discos.